THE SMALL SINGER

by Roberta McLaughlin
and Lucille Wood

Illustrated by Jacques Rupp

BOWMAR

Phonograph albums of the following songs appearing in this volume are available:

ALBUM 1:

Little Creatures
Grandfather Frog
The Snail
A Frog Went Walking
Rabbit
Lady Bug

Wheels and Wings
Big Black Train
Chug Chug Chug
Fire Truck
I Can Fly

Songs of Mexico
A Jump
When You Sing
I Like It

Play
Ride Cowboy Ride
Giddiap
A Little Girl
The Band
Balloons for Sale
Barnacle Bill
Merry Go Round
Don't Cry Little Dolly
Little Shadow
Dance in a Circle

Halloween
Halloween Sounds
I'm a Witch
Three Black Cats

ALBUM 2:

Nature
Poor Mister Wind
Song of the Wind
Bend With the Wind
Raindrops
Lullaby of the Rain
Fog
Star Bright
Little Shell

Pets
Mr. Turtle
Trot Old Joe
Playmates
Kitty and Puppy

Seasons
Autumn Dances
We Are Thankful
A World of Snow
Christmas is Coming
Little Lamb
Ding-A-Ling-A-Ling
Easter Bells
Easter Rabbit
I Know It's Spring
Love Somebody
Patriotic Medley

Home
Skip to Market
When Is the Day

Albums may be ordered from:

Bowmar Records, Inc., 622 Rodier Drive, Glendale, Calif. 91201

First Printing . . . . .March 1969
Second Printing . . . . .February 1972

PREFACE

To Teachers of Small Singers,

This collection includes songs that our small singers have enjoyed year after year. Familiar and new songs with varied musical activities give the children a head start in the love and understanding of music.

There are repeated refrains which encourage immediate response and help small singers find their singing voices. Many simple repeated patterns may be played on the bells. Some songs invite movement, others lend themselves to a percussion accompaniment.

There are songs for singing throughout the day and year. "A Tea Party" is a song for the playhouse, "My Little Red Car" for playing in the sand. Marching and singing "The Patriotic Medley" is a good way to start the day and "Don't Cry Little Dolly" is a relaxing rest time song. Alternating periods of rest and activity are provided in "Tiptoe Song" and "Lullaby of the Rain."

We believe that in addition to the obvious musical learnings implicit in these songs, they can contribute to the growth of young children in other ways. What better way can mathematical concepts be reinforced than with singing songs like "Raindrops"? "Mister Turtle" and "World of Snow" make the very young child become more aware of the world around him. "Easter Rabbit" and "Fire Truck" teach children to follow a story sequence.

If English is a second language for the child all of these songs will provide a pleasurable introduction to the language.

The happy attitude established through singing provides the ideal climate for learning. We hope that you will discover some old favorite songs in this collection and that many of its new songs will become favorites of your small singers.

Roberta McLaughlin

Lucille Wood

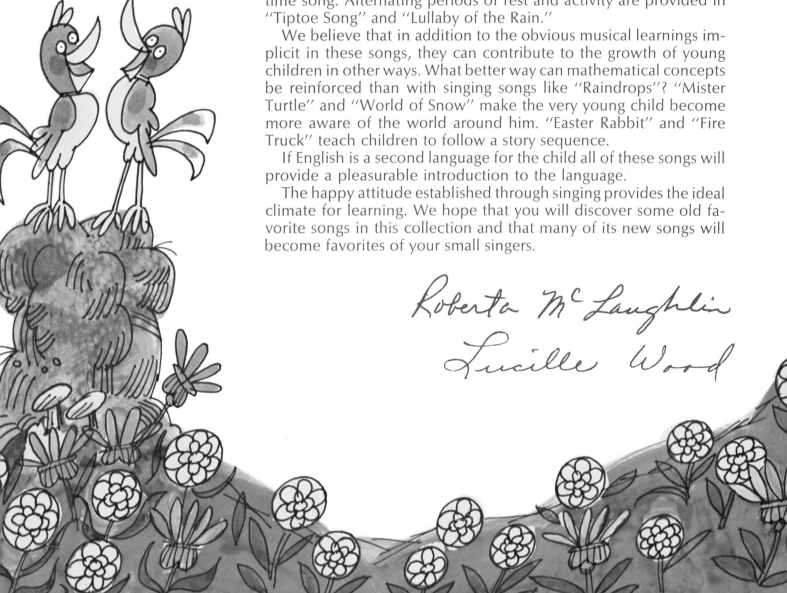

TABLE OF CONTENTS

Clap with Me

Traditional

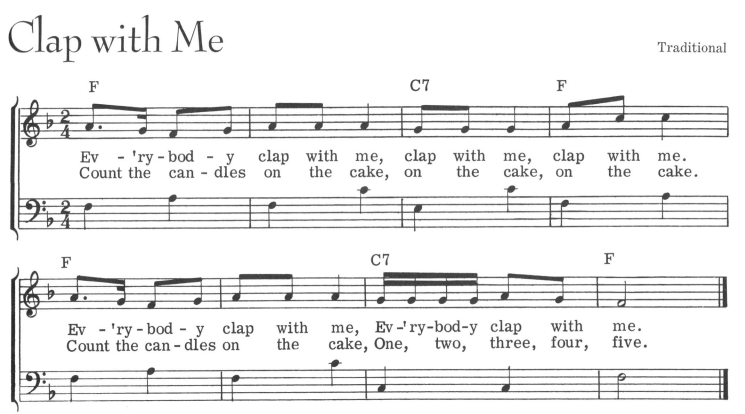

Ev - 'ry-bod - y clap with me, clap with me, clap with me.
Count the can - dles on the cake, on the cake, on the cake.

Ev - 'ry-bod - y clap with me, Ev-'ry-bod-y clap with me.
Count the can - dles on the cake, One, two, three, four, five.

Each day sing about a new experience to this favorite melody of small singers.

Mary Had a Little Lamb

Traditional

Ma - ry had a lit - tle lamb, lit - tle lamb, lit - tle lamb.
Jin - gle jin - gle sil - ver bell, sil - ver bell, sil - ver bell.

Ma - ry had a lit - tle lamb, Its fleece was white as snow.
Jin - gle jin - gle sil - ver bell,___ Jingle jingle sil - ver bell.

Each child will want a turn to jingle the silver bell tied to a ribbon around the neck of a little toy lamb.

7

Up Up in the Sky

Unknown

Smoothly   F (One strum per measure)

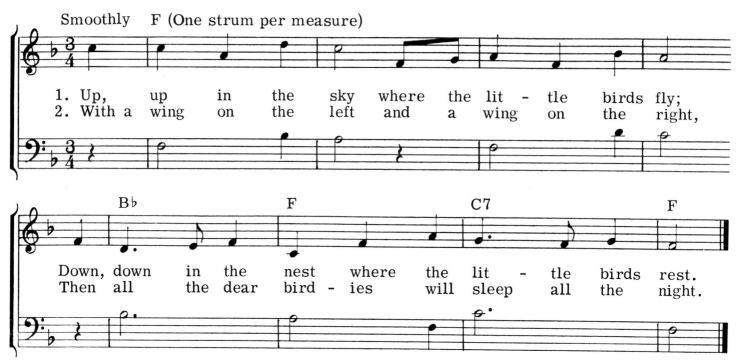

1. Up,   up   in   the   sky   where   the   lit - tle   birds   fly;
2. With a wing   on   the   left   and   a   wing   on   the   right,

Bb   F   C7   F

Down, down   in   the   nest   where   the   lit - tle   birds   rest.
Then   all   the   dear   bird - ies   will   sleep   all   the   night.

3. When the big sun comes up and the clouds roll away,
   Then all the dear birdies will play all the day.

4. When the big sun comes up and the clouds roll away,
   "Good morning, good morning," the little birds say.

Two Little Blackbirds

Traditional

Two lit-tle black-birds sit-ting on a hill, One named Jack, One named Jill.

Fly a-way, Jack, fly a-way, Jill; Come back, Jack, come back, Jill.

Pretend that the two forefingers are the two blackbirds; let them fly behind the back and return. Or, dramatize the song with two children taking the roles of the blackbirds.

Sing Little Birdie

Trudi Behar

Lightly

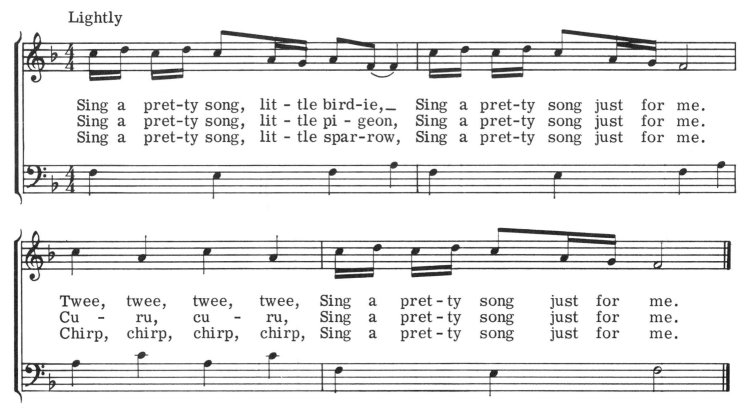

Sing a pret-ty song, lit-tle bird-ie,_ Sing a pret-ty song just for me.
Sing a pret-ty song, lit-tle pi - geon, Sing a pret-ty song just for me.
Sing a pret-ty song, lit-tle spar-row, Sing a pret-ty song just for me.

Twee, twee, twee, twee, Sing a pret-ty song just for me.
Cu - ru, cu - ru, Sing a pret-ty song just for me.
Chirp, chirp, chirp, chirp, Sing a pret-ty song just for me.

Play the bells with the bird sounds. The same pitches may be played as an introduction, accompaniment and coda.

Three Owls

R.M.

One lit - tle owl said, "Whoo, whoo," Two lit - tle owls said, "Whoo, whoo,

Three lit - tle owls said, "Whoo, whoo," As they sat in the old oak tree.

Give one child the D bell, another the F bell and another the A bell. Play with the words "whoo, whoo", as indicated by the notation or with the entire song.

"Who would like to play the D bell as we sing 'whoo, whoo'?"
"Now we add the F bell."
"Listen for all three bells when we add the A."

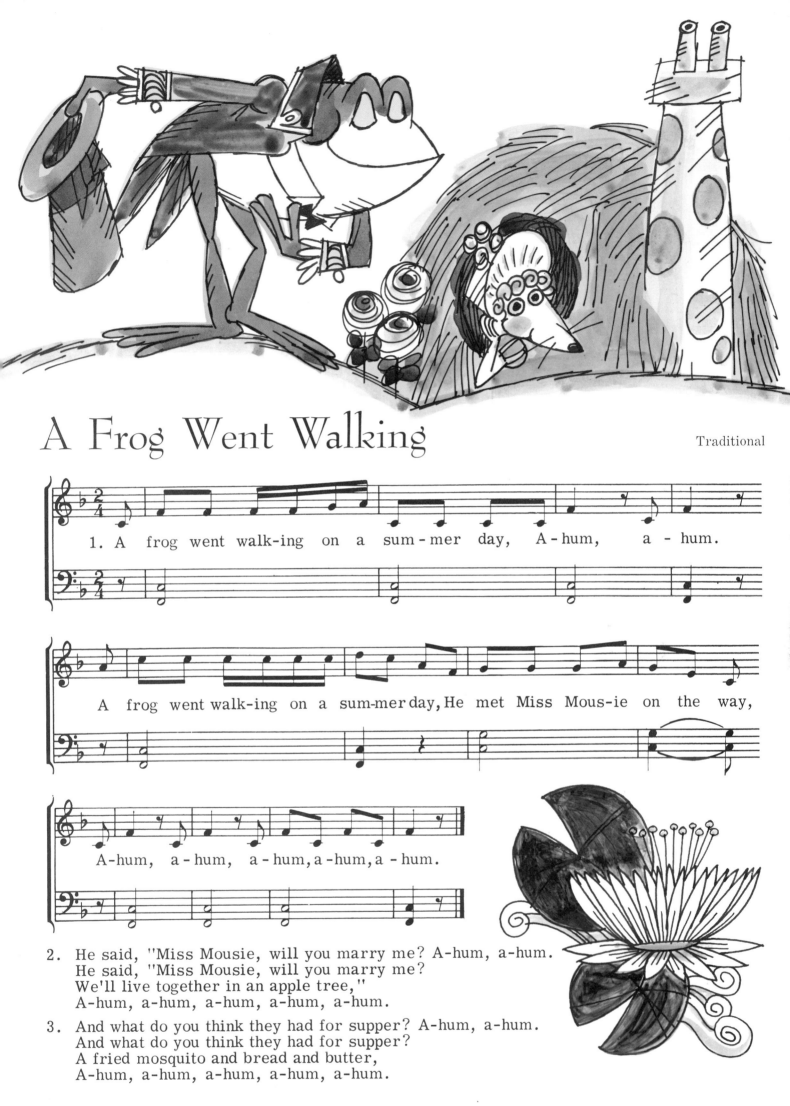

A Frog Went Walking

Traditional

1. A frog went walk-ing on a sum-mer day, A-hum, a-hum.
A frog went walk-ing on a sum-mer day, He met Miss Mous-ie on the way,
A-hum, a-hum, a-hum, a-hum, a-hum.

2. He said, "Miss Mousie, will you marry me? A-hum, a-hum.
   He said, "Miss Mousie, will you marry me?
   We'll live together in an apple tree,"
   A-hum, a-hum, a-hum, a-hum, a-hum.

3. And what do you think they had for supper? A-hum, a-hum.
   And what do you think they had for supper?
   A fried mosquito and bread and butter,
   A-hum, a-hum, a-hum, a-hum, a-hum.

Grandfather Frog

L.W.

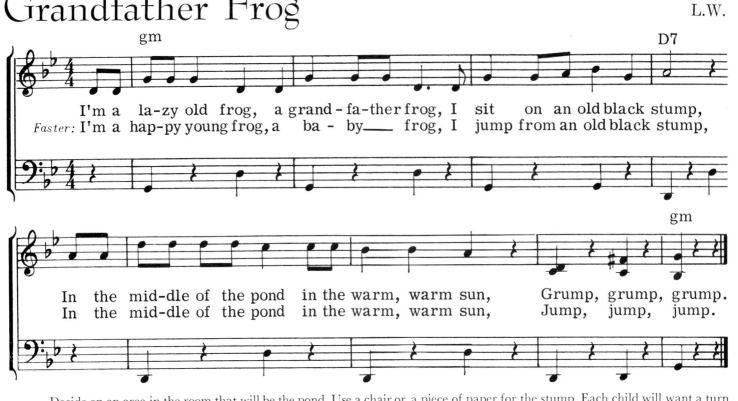

I'm a la-zy old frog, a grand-fa-ther frog, I sit on an old black stump,
Faster: I'm a hap-py young frog, a ba - by___ frog, I jump from an old black stump,

In the mid-dle of the pond in the warm, warm sun, Grump, grump, grump.
In the mid-dle of the pond in the warm, warm sun, Jump, jump, jump.

Decide on an area in the room that will be the pond. Use a chair or a piece of paper for the stump. Each child will want a turn being one of the frogs.

Dicky Ducky Duddle

Moiselle Renstrom

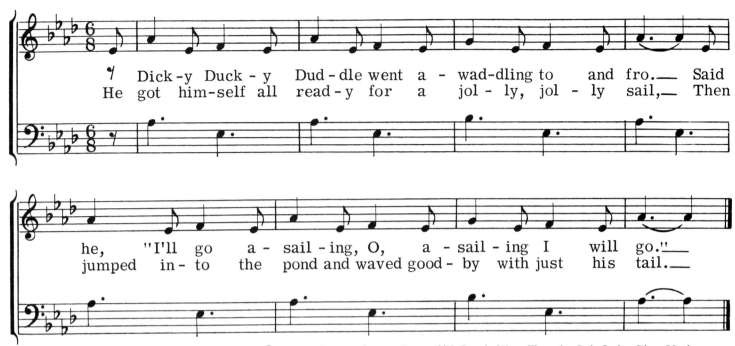

Dick-y Duck-y Dud-dle went a - wad-dling to and fro.— Said
He got him-self all read-y for a jol - ly, jol - ly sail,— Then

he, "I'll go a - sail-ing, O, a - sail - ing I will go."—
jumped in - to the pond and waved good - by with just his tail.—

Come to the Farm

Trudi Behar

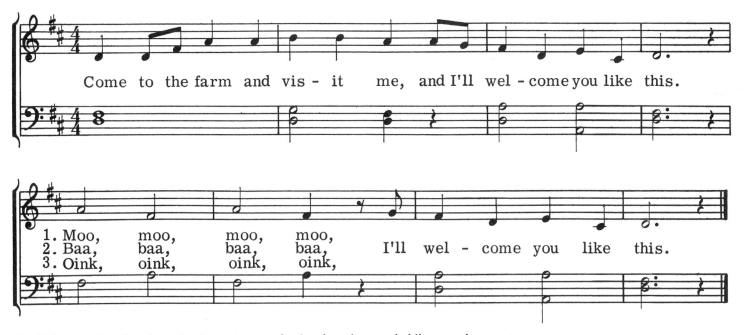

Come to the farm and vis - it   me, and I'll wel - come you like this.

1. Moo,   moo,   moo,   moo,
2. Baa,   baa,   baa,   baa,   I'll wel - come you like this.
3. Oink,   oink,   oink,   oink,

Small singers often sing the animal sounds more freely when they are holding a sack puppet.
Play the bells with the animal sounds.

Swim Little Duck!

R.M.

1. Swim, lit-tle duck, Swim lit-tle duck,   swim,   swim,   swim.

Swim, lit-tle duck, swim, lit - tle duck,   swim,   swim,   swim.

2. Fly, little duck, etc.

3. Sleep, little duck, etc.

"How can you show what the little duck is doing?" "What else can a little duck do?" (Peck, eat, etc.)

Rabbit

L.W.

There was an old rab-bit lived un-der a hill, Ho, hum, fid-dle dee dee.

And some folks say that he's liv-ing there still, Ho, hum, fid-dle dee, dee.

This lit-tle old rab-bit would dance all night, Play and dance in the bright moon-light

Ho, hum, fid - dle dee dee. Ho, hum, fid - dle dee dee.

The children may create a hippity-hop rabbit dance to the refrain.

The Children's Zoo

L.W.

1. How do you do? How do you do? We are glad to see you.
2. I am a duck, I am a duck, I am glad to see you.
3. I am a hen, I am a hen, I am glad to see you.

Welcome, welcome to our zoo, O - pen the gate and come on through.
2. Wad - dle, wad-dle, quack, quack, quack, Wad-dle, ___ wad - dle, quack, quack, quack.
   Pa - to, pa - to, qua, qua, qua, Pa - to, ___ pa - to, qua, qua, qua.
3. Peck and peck and cluck, cluck, cluck, Peck and ___ peck and cluck, cluck, cluck.

How do you do? How do you do? We are glad to see you.
I am a duck, I am a duck, I am glad to see you.
I am a hen, I am a hen, I am glad to see you.

Sing about other animals in the children's zoo.
Substitute or add the Spanish names of animals, such as "el conejo" or "el burrito".
Use sack puppets to make the animals sing.

Fuzzy Wuzzy Caterpillar

R.M.
Acc. by Leslie Wilbur

1. Fuz-zy wuz-zy cat-er-pil-lar humps a - long,
2. Fuz-zy wuz-zy cat-er-pil-lar goes to sleep,
3. Some-day you will be a pret-ty but - ter - fly,

humps a - long, humps a - long; Fuz-zy wuz-zy cat-er-pil-lar
goes to sleep, goes to sleep; Fuz-zy wuz-zy cat-er-pil-lar
but - ter-fly, but - ter-fly; Some day you will be a pret-ty

humps a - long, Out to see the world._____
goes to sleep In a warm co - coon._____
but - ter - fly, Out to see the world._____

Firefly

Trudi Behar

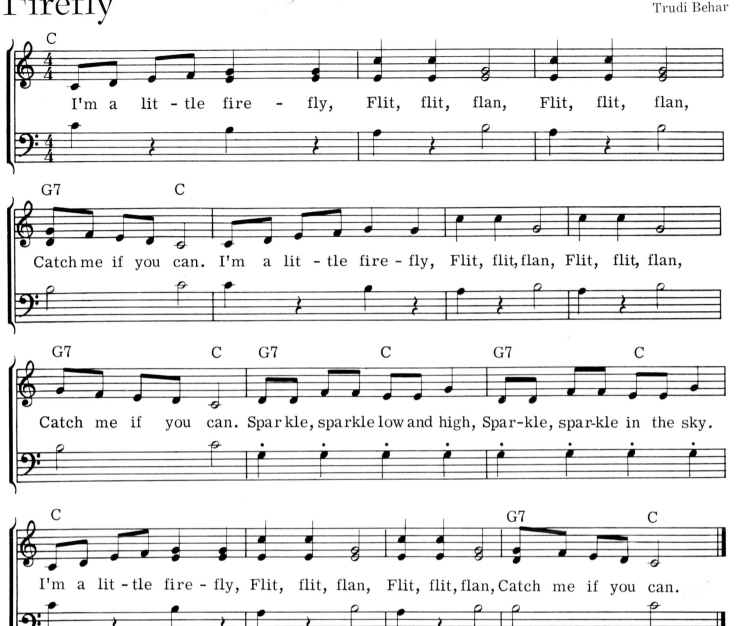

I'm a lit-tle fire-fly, Flit, flit, flan, Flit, flit, flan,

Catch me if you can. I'm a lit-tle fire-fly, Flit, flit, flan, Flit, flit, flan,

Catch me if you can. Sparkle, sparkle low and high, Spar-kle, spar-kle in the sky.

I'm a lit-tle fire-fly, Flit, flit, flan, Flit, flit, flan, Catch me if you can.

"What part of the song can you play on the bells?"
Finger cymbals make a sparkling accompaniment.

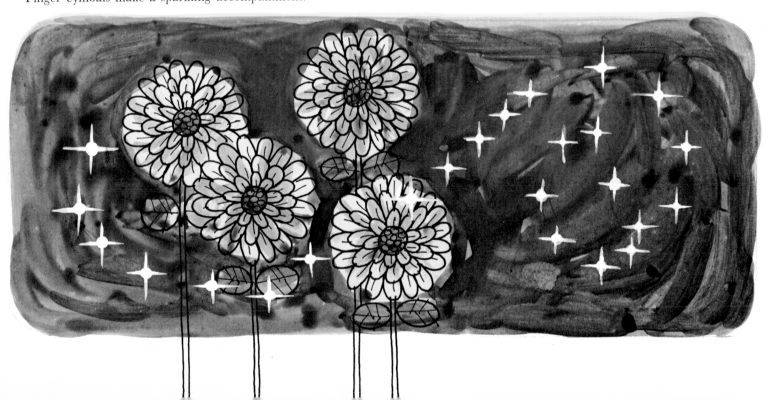

Ladybug

Wilhelmina Seegmiller
& Otto Miessner

With a swing

Verse 1 (top line):
La - dy - bug, la - dy - bug, how do you do?
How do you do? How do you do?
La - dy - bug, la - dy - bug, fly a - way, shoo!
Fly a - way, fly a - way!

Verse 2 (bottom line):
Your lit - tle chil - dren are sleep - ing so snug,
Sleep - ing so snug, Sleep - ing so snug;
Bet - ter go home now, you bad lit - tle bug,
Bet - ter go home right now!

Here is the Beehive

Traditional

Here is the bee-hive, where are the bees? Hid-den a-way where no-bod-y sees.

Watch and you'll see them come out of the hive, One, two, three, four, five.

Make a beehive of the clenched fist and release one finger with each number. The song lends itself to the use of feltboard figures or paper sack puppets.

The Bee

Old Tune

There was a bee sat on a wall, He said he could hum and that was all. Mm ___

Sing other stanzas, such as

mosquito - buzz
boy - whistle
girl - "la, la"

Little Shell

R.M.

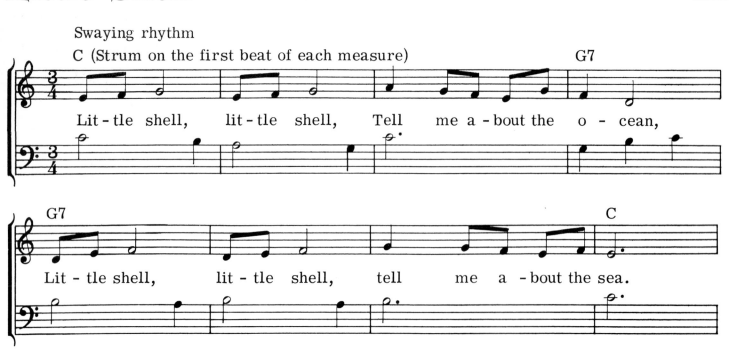

Swaying rhythm

C (Strum on the first beat of each measure)   G7

Lit - tle shell, lit - tle shell, Tell me a - bout the o - cean,

G7   C

Lit - tle shell, lit - tle shell, tell me a - bout the sea.

1. Where have you been? Where is your home?
2. Cor - al and kelp, Sea - weed and sand,

Lit - tle shell, lit - tle shell that the waves brought to me.

"Hold a make-believe shell to your ear as you sing."
"What else would you find in the ocean?"
"As you listen to the recording, be a little shell and sway as the waves rock you."

25

Snail Snail

R.M.

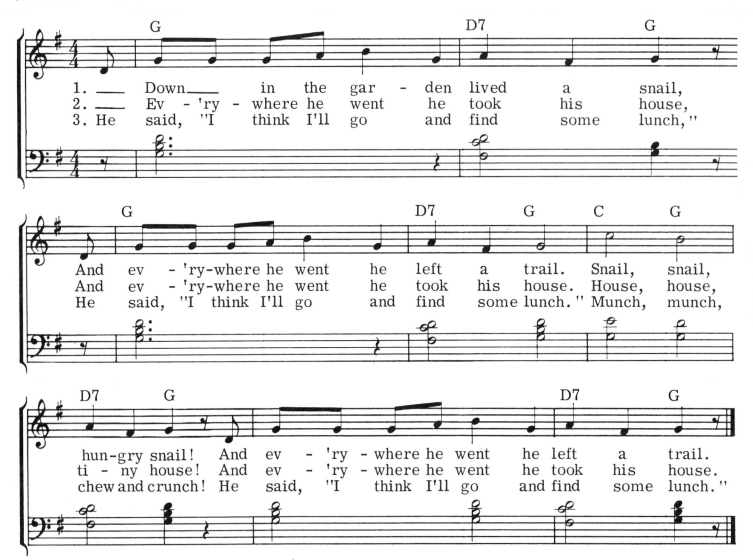

1. ___ Down ___ in the gar - den lived a snail,
2. ___ Ev - 'ry - where he went he took his house,
3. He said, "I think I'll go and find some lunch,"

And ev - 'ry-where he went he left a trail. Snail, snail,
And ev - 'ry-where he went he took his house. House, house,
He said, "I think I'll go and find some lunch." Munch, munch,

hun-gry snail! And ev - 'ry - where he went he left a trail.
ti - ny house! And ev - 'ry - where he went he took his house.
chew and crunch! He said, "I think I'll go and find some lunch."

"Which phrases are alike?" "Which phrase is different?"

A book to share with the children: "You Can Find a Snail" by Miller and Seligman. Holt, Rinehart and Winston.

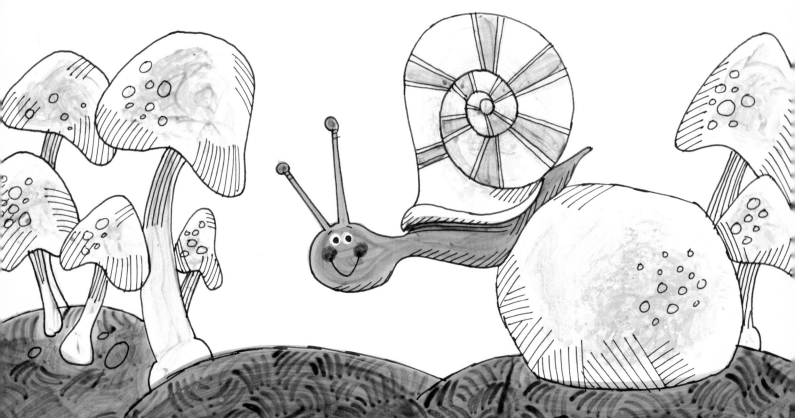

How Many Raindrops?

Trudi Behar

The pitter patter notes (d and a) make an effective accompaniment played throughout the entire song. Tiny rhythm sticks make an effective rain sound. Play the bells on f - c - d at the end of each phrase. The d minor chord may be played on the autoharp on first and third beats.

Raindrops

L.W.

3. Three little raindrops knocking on the roof, etc.

4. Four little raindrops dancing up and down, etc.

5. Five little raindrops sliding down the pane, etc.

6. Six little raindrops sleeping in the sun, etc.

7. Seven little raindrops run away and hide, etc.

"Show how the little raindrops move as we sing."
"Choose an instrument that will sound like raindrops knocking on the roof."

It Rained a Mist

Folk Song from Virginia

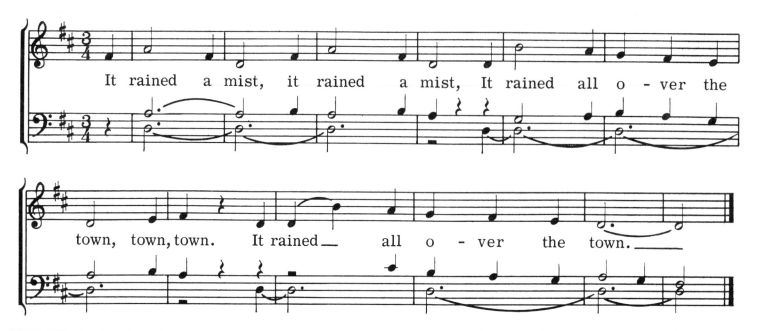

Sing about all the things that happened after the rain: About the sun, wind, flowers, children playing, children going to sleep at night, the stars shining and the moon coming up. The last verses may be sung very softly to counteract the excitement of a rainy day. For example:

The stars came out, the stars came out,
They shone all over the town, town, town,
They shone all over the town.

Fog

L.W.

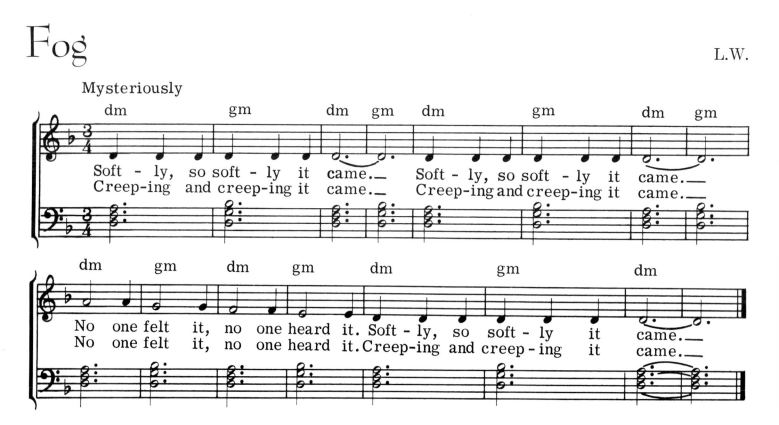

"Show by the way you move how it would feel to be a cold, silent, misty fog."

Lullaby of the Rain

L.W.

Quietly

The rain sings a lull - a - by, qui -
The moon sails be - hind the clouds, qui -

et - ly, soft - ly; The rain sings a
et - ly, soft - ly; The moon sails be -

lull - a - by, Go to sleep.____
hind the clouds, Go to sleep.____

On a Rainy Day

Traditional

1. Ev - 'ry - bod - y clap your hands, clap your hands, clap your hands.
2. Ev - 'ry - bod - y tap your toes, tap your toes, tap your toes.

Ev - 'ry-bod - y clap your hands, On a rain - y day.
Ev - 'ry-bod - y tap your toes, On a rain - y day.

3. Ev'rybody stand and stretch, etc.
4. Ev'rybody rest awhile, etc.

Bend with the Wind

R.M.

Swinging rhythm

1. Bend with the wind, bend with the wind. Sway____
2. Fall with the leaves, fall with the leaves. Fall____

sway____ and bend, bend with the wind.____
fall____ and fall, fall with the leaves.____

"Reach as high as the tallest tree as you sway with the wind."

Song of the Wind

L.W.

1. Ooo_____ Ooo_____ the wind is sing-ing a song to you.
2. Ooo_____ Ooo_____ oh, what a blus-ter-y, wind-y day.

(Echo)

Ooo_____ Ooo_____ the wind is sing-ing to you.
Ooo_____ Ooo_____ *come bring your kite___ and play.-

(Echo)

*In the Fall of the year substitute "he blows the leaves away."

Poor Mister Wind

L.W.

Sadly

1. Poor Mis-ter Wind! Poor Mis-ter Wind Has lost his hap-py song,___
2. Poor Mis-ter Wind! Poor Mis-ter Wind! He lost it in the tree-tops,
3. Poor Mis-ter Wind! Poor Mis-ter Wind! The rain is cry-ing soft-ly,

Has lost his hap-py song.___ Poor Mis-ter Wind! Poor Mis-ter Wind!
He lost it in the tree-tops. Poor Mis-ter Wind! Poor Mis-ter Wind!
The rain is cry-ing soft-ly. Poor Mis-ter Wind! Poor Mis-ter Wind!

Play the first two and last two measures on the bells.

A World of Snow

R.M.

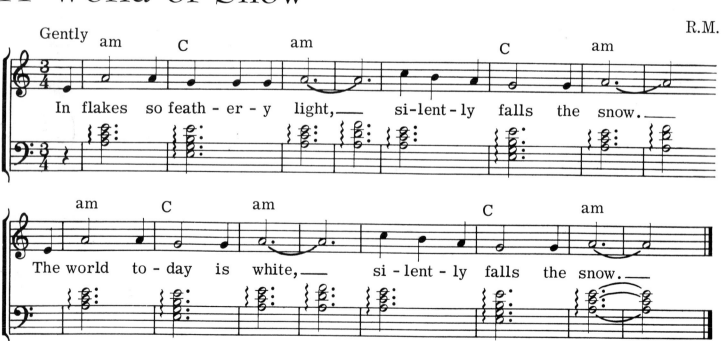

In flakes so feath-er-y light,___ si-lent-ly falls the snow.___

The world to-day is white,___ si-lent-ly falls the snow.___

"Would you like to be dancing snowflakes as you listen to the music? Remember that no one hears the snow."
"As you listen to the recording, find out how the sound of the celeste is like falling snowflakes."

Snow

L.W.

The snow is piled so high,___ The snow is piled so high.___

White on the ground, white in the sky. The snow is piled so high,___

___ The snow is piled so high.___

Aiken Drum

Traditional
Scottish

1. There was a man lived in the moon, lived in the moon, lived in the moon, There was a man lived in the moon, and his name was Ai - ken Drum.

CHORUS: And he played upon a ladle, a ladle, a ladle,
And he played upon a ladle, and his name was Aiken Drum.

2. And his hat was made of cream cheese, etc.
3. And his coat was made of good roast beef, etc.

Add your own verses. Of what were his shoes made? His shirt? His tie? Play rhythm instruments on the chorus.

Star Bright

Traditional
L.W.

Star bright, star light, First star I see to-night One bright star. I wish I may, I wish I might have the wish I wish to-night, Good night star.

"Choose an instrument with a tinkling sound to play on the repeated tones."

I'm a Witch

L.W.

Mysteriously

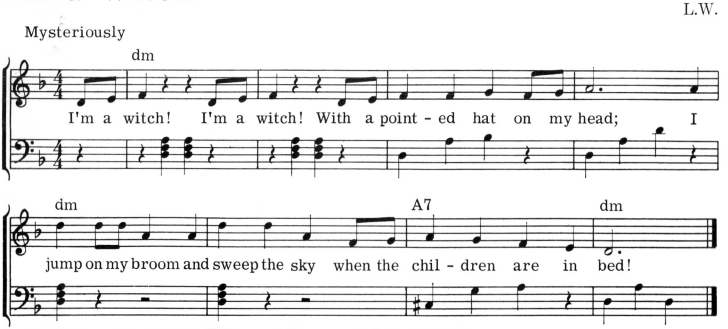

I'm a witch! I'm a witch! With a point - ed hat on my head; I jump on my broom and sweep the sky when the chil - dren are in bed!

"Listen for a Halloween sound on the recording and choose an instrument to imitate it while you are singing."

Three Black Cats

Jeanne S. Davis

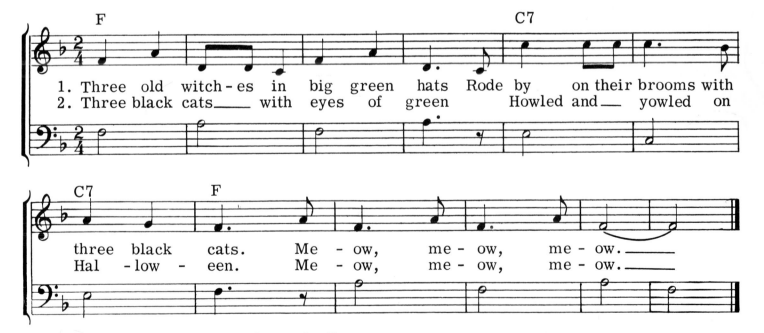

1. Three old witch-es in big green hats Rode by on their brooms with three black cats. Me - ow, me - ow, me - ow.
2. Three black cats with eyes of green Howled and yowled on Hal - low - een. Me - ow, me - ow, me - ow.

"What instrument plays the 'meows' on the recording?" (Violin)

39

The Little Pumpkin

R.M.

A round lit - tle pump - kin grew in the sun,

He grew and he grew to a big, big one.

He grew and he grew and be - came on Hal - low - e'en

The best jack - o - lan - tern ev - er seen!

One Two Three

R.M.

One, two, three, owls in a tree; One, two, three, can't scare me!

Take C, D and E out of the resonator bell set for ease of playing. Sing with letter names, too: c d e, c d e, c d e, e d c.

40

Halloween Sounds

Louise Scott
Lucille Wood

1. This is the way—— the witch - es fly, witch - es fly, witch - es fly.
2. This is the way—— the ghosts go by, ghosts go by, ghosts go by.

This is the way—— the witch - es fly, Swish, swish, swish.
This is the way—— the ghosts go by, Oh! Oh! Oh!

3. This is the way the tomcats howl, tomcats howl, tomcats howl.
   This is the way the tomcats howl, Meow! Meow! Meow!

4. This is the way the pumpkins laugh, pumpkins laugh, pumpkins laugh.
   This is the way the pumpkins laugh, Hee! Hee! Hee!

5. This is the way the hoot owls cry, hoot owls cry, hoot owls cry.
   This is the way the hoot owls cry, Hoo, hoo, hoo.

The Witches

Arlene Schroeder

The witch-es are com-ing to-night! The witch-es are com-ing to - night!—

They ride on a broom up, up to the moon, The witch-es are com-ing to-night!—

"Gallop on your broom."

A Pumpkin Man

L.W.

1. With one round eye I'm a pump - kin man,
2. With two round eyes I'm a pump - kin man,

With one round eye I can wink, I can.
With two round eyes I can see, I can.

3. With a funny nose I'm a pumpkin man,
   With a funny nose I can sniff, I can.

4. With a curvy mouth I'm a pumpkin man,
   With a curvy mouth I can smile, I can.

5. With a candle light I'm a pumpkin man,
   With a candle light I can shine, I can.

Autumn Dance

Amalia Willis

Smoothly

1. Danc-ing like the leaves____ Fall - ing from the trees.____
2. Sway-ing like the trees____ Shak - ing all the leaves.____

Round and round and round and round, Danc - ing like the leaves.____
Back and forth and back and forth, Sway - ing like the leaves.____

(Faster) 3. Skipping like the breeze, Scattering the leaves;
Up and down and up and down, Skipping like the breeze.

Choose one group to be the leaves, another to be the trees.
"Think of many ways a leaf moves when the wind blows."

Big Tall Indian

Satis Coleman

Accented

This is how the big tall In-dian

beats up-on his drum.

Ho, ho, hi, hi,

ho, ho, hi.

Three Turkeys

L.W.

1. The night be-fore Thanks-giv-ing, When I had gone to bed, I
5. Then on Thanks-giv-ing morn-ing, When the farm-er came a-round, Those

heard three tur-key gob-blers, and this is what they said.
three tur-key gob-blers could not be found.

2. The first__ tur-key said, "I think that I will go
3. The sec-ond tur-key said, "I think I'll find a tree
4. The third__ tur-key said, "I think it would be fun

And
And
To

hide be-hind the hay-stack Where no one will know."
hide up in the branch-es Where no one will see."
hide the farm-er's hatch-et, Then run, run, run, run."

The children will enjoy dramatizing the song.
"Find a good spot in the room for the haystack, the tree and the hatchet."

45

Gobble Gobble

L.W.

Come, come, come and see Tur - key gob - blers in a tree. "Gob - ble, gob - ble, gob - ble, gob - ble," hear them say, "You can't catch us on Thanks - giv - ing Day."

We Are Thankful

R.M.

Reverently

We are thank - ful in our work and play.

We are thank - ful on Thanks - giv - ing Day.

46

Winter Holiday

Trudi Behar

Ding, ding, ding, a win-ter hol-i-day, Ding, ding, ding, a jol-ly hol-i-day. Some call it Christ-mas, some call it Han-nu-kah,

Can-dles for Christ-mas, can-dles for Han-nu-kah,
Pres-ents for Christ-mas, pres-ents for Han-nu-kah, Ding, ding, ding, a
Par-ties for Christ-mas, par-ties for Han-nu-kah,

win-ter hol-i-day, Ding, ding, ding, a jol-ly hol-i-day.

Candles of Hannukah

Adapted by RM and LW

1. Burn, lit-tle can-dles, burn, burn, burn, Han-nu-kah is here.
2. Eight lit-tle can-dles in a row, Han-nu-kah is here.
3. Dance, lit-tle can-dles, dance, dance, dance, Han-nu-kah is here.

Burn, lit-tle can-dles, burn, burn, burn, Burn-ing bright and clear.
Eight lit-tle can-dles in a row, Burn-ing bright and clear.
Dance, lit-tle can-dles, dance, dance, dance, Burn-ing bright and clear.

Hannukah is a Jewish holiday that lasts for eight days. One candle is lighted each night in a candelabra called a Menorah. Invite children to stand like candles in the Menorah. They may imitate the dancing flame with hands touching over their heads.

Reprinted from "Sing A Song", by Lucille Wood and Roberta McLaughlin, © 1968 by Bowmar Records, Inc.

Christmas is Coming

L.W.

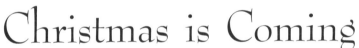

Merrily

G   am   D7   G

1. Christ-mas is com-ing, Christ-mas is com-ing! See the can-dles glow.
2. Christ-mas is com-ing, Christ-mas is com-ing! Hear the sleigh-bells ring!

G   am   D7   G

Christ-mas is com-ing, Christ-mas is com-ing! Lights a-cross the snow.
Christ-mas is com-ing, Christ-mas is com-ing! Hear the chil-dren sing.

"What sounds of Christmas are heard in the recording?" "Play sleighbells as an introduction, accompaniment and coda."

Little Lamb

R.M.

Tenderly

Lit - tle lamb, lit - tle lamb, ly - ing on the hill - side,

Lit - tle lamb, lit - tle lamb,
What did you see?
What did you hear?
Where did you go?

G   am

"I   saw   the   light   of   a   bright   star
"I   heard the   song   of   the   an   -   gels
"I   went to   see   the   dear Ba   -   by

D7   G

Shin - ing   down   on   me."_____
Sing - ing   sweet   and   clear."_____
Born   so   long   a - go."_____

One group, or a small singer, may sing the question and another the answer.

51

Ding-A-Ling-A-Ling

L.W.

Merrily

1. San - ta's com - ing in his sleigh, Ding - a - ling - a - ling ring the
2. Christ - mas trees on Christ - mas lane, Ding - a - ling - a - ling ring the

Christ - mas bells. Ho! Ho! Ho! he's___ on ___ his way,
Christ - mas bells. Chug, chug, chug, goes the lit - tle toy train,

Ding - a - ling - a - ling ring the Christ - mas bells.
Ding - a - ling - a - ling ring the Christ - mas bells.

"Make up other words for the first and third phrases."

Christmas Tree

R.M.

Christ - mas tree, Christ - mas tree, Beau - ti - ful, spark - ling Christ - mas tree,
Christ - mas bell, Christ - mas bell, Beau - ti - ful, spark - ling Christ - mas bell,

Christ - mas tree, Christ - mas tree, Hap - py, shin - ing tree!__
Christ - mas bell, Christ - mas bell, Hap - py, shin - ing bell!__

Love Somebody

American Folk Song

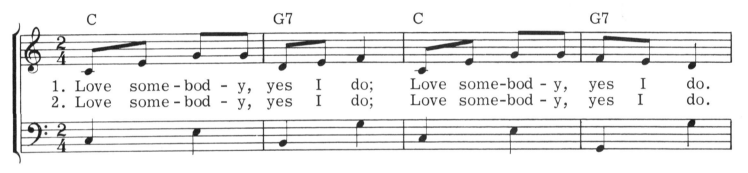

1. Love some-bod - y, yes I do; Love some-bod - y, yes I do.
2. Love some-bod - y, yes I do; Love some-bod - y, yes I do.

Love some-bod - y, yes I do; Love some-bod-y, but I won't tell who.
Love some-bod - y, yes I do; Love some-bod-y, but you can't guess who.

Counting Valentines

One lit - tle val-en-tine, two lit - tle val-en-tines, three lit - tle val - en-tines,

four lit - tle val - en-tines, five lit - tle val - en-tines all for you.

Valentine Dance

Trudi Behar

Gaily

Won't you be my val - en - tine, my val - en - tine, please do, ___

Say that you like me, and I will say that I like you. ___

Let me take your right hand, let me take your left hand;

To - geth - er let us skip and skip to Val - en - tine Land.

"Make up a valentine dance."

54

St. Patrick's Day

Traditional

1. We're wear-ing green for the I - rish, We're wear-ing green for the
2. We'll dance a jig for the I - rish, We'll dance a jig for the

I - rish. We're wear-ing green for the I - rish On this St. Pat - rick's Day.
I - rish. We'll dance a jig for the I - rish On this St. Pat - rick's Day.

Other traditional stanzas:
Me fither and mither were Irish, etc.
And I am Irish, too.

We kept a pig in the parlor, etc.
And he is Irish, too.

Birthday Song

Traditional
Adapted

On this bright and hap-py day A morn-ing song we sing to you,

Hap-py birth-day, dear Juan-i-ta, May all your wish-es come true.
to dear Jean,

This is the melody of a popular birthday song in Mexico which many Spanish speaking children may recognize.

Easter Bells

Roberta Stong

Ding! Dong! Ding! Dong! Church bells sing an Eas - ter song.

Hear them as they soft - ly ring, Hear the chil - dren sweet - ly sing.

Church bells ring and chil - dren sing an Eas - ter song.

Ding! Dong! Ding! Dong! Ding! Dong! Ding! Dong!

"Play the 'ding dong' pitches on the resonator bells as an introduction, as an accompaniment on the first, third and fourth phrases and as a coda." (b flat and e flat)

I Know It's Spring

R.M.

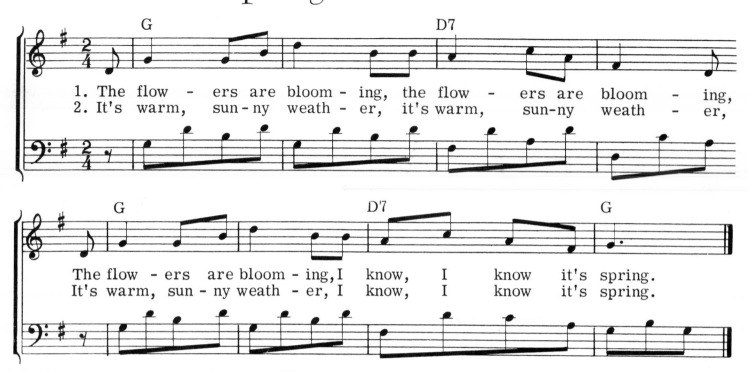

1. The flow - ers are bloom - ing, the flow - ers are bloom - ing,
2. It's warm, sun - ny weath - er, it's warm, sun - ny weath - er,

The flow - ers are bloom - ing, I know, I know it's spring.
It's warm, sun - ny weath - er, I know, I know it's spring.

Create other verses, such as: The new colt is playing, the new chicks are peeping, etc.
"What other signs tell us that spring is here?"

Easter Rabbit

Traditional
Elizabeth Jung

1. A lit - tle rab - bit came to town, came to town, came to town.
2. He carried a bas - ket in his hand, in his hand, in his hand.

A lit - tle rab - bit came to town, Hop, hop, hop.
He carried a bas - ket in his hand, Hop, hop, hop.

3. We followed him around the town, 'round the town, 'round the town.
   We followed him around the town, Hop, hop, hop.

4. The little rabbit hid his eggs, hid his eggs, hid his eggs.
   The little rabbit hid his eggs, Hop, hop, hop.

5. On Easter Day we found the eggs, found the eggs, found the eggs.
   On Easter Day we found the eggs, Hop, hop, hop.

6. We thank you for the Easter eggs, Easter eggs, Easter eggs.
   We thank you for the Easter eggs, Hop, hop, hop.

Little Prairie Dog

Hopi Children's Song
Collected by Mildred Frazee

Lit - tle prai - rie dog, lit - tle prai - rie dog, sit - ting on the ground,

sit - ting on the ground, Lit - tle prai - rie dog, lit - tle prai - rie dog,

sit - ting on the ground, sit - ting on the ground, Sing - ing to you,

sing - ing to me, "Spring is here, spring is here,

Lis - ten to it! Lis - ten to it! Nik! Nik! Nik!

This song may be taught and sung as an echo song.

From North American Indian Songs by Muriel Dawley and Roberta McLaughlin. ©1961 Highland Press. Used by permission.

59

A Little Girl

French Folk Tune
L.W.

1. A lit - tle girl was skip - ping, Tra la la la la
2. A lit - tle boy was walk-ing, Tra la la la la

la la la, A lit - tle girl was skip - ping, Tra
la la la, A lit - tle boy was walk - ing, Tra

la la la la la la la, Tra la la la la la.___
la la la la la la la, Tra la la la la la.___

3. And ev'ryone was singing, etc.

"Choose an instrument to play a skipping rhythm, another to play a walking rhythm:

Barnacle Bill

Sung by children in Canada

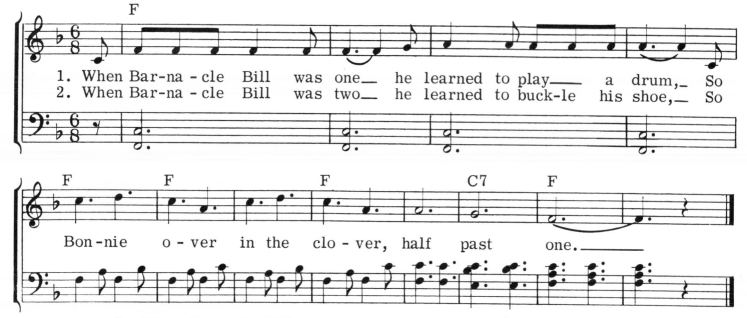

1. When Bar-na-cle Bill was one— he learned to play— a drum,— So
2. When Bar-na-cle Bill was two— he learned to buck-le his shoe,— So

Bon-nie o-ver in the clo-ver, half past one.____

3. When Barnacle Bill was three he learned to climb a tree, etc.

4. When Barnacle Bill was four he learned to scrub the floor, etc.

5. When Barnacle Bill was five he learned to swim and dive, etc.

On the words "half past one," the children swing the right foot over the ball as it bounces.

Dance in a Circle

L.W.
R.M.

1. Dance in a cir-cle, round we go. Ha! Ha! Ha! Ho! Ho! Ho!
3. Clap all to-geth-er, one two three. Ha! Ha! Ha! Hee! Hee! Hee!

2. In to the cen-ter, in we go. Right back out, Ho! Ho! Ho!
4. Stamp all to-geth-er, one two three. Ha! Ha! Ha! Ho! Ho! Ho!

5. Dance in a circle, round we go. Ha! Ha! Ha! Ho! Ho! Ho!

"Listen to the banjo on the recording."
The recording provides an instrumental phrase for each activity.

Skip to Market

L.W.

1. Please skip down to the mar-ket, oh, the mar-ket, oh, mar-ket, oh.
2. Please skip back from the mar-ket, oh, the mar-ket, oh, mar-ket, oh.

Please skip down to the mar - ket, oh, To buy a pound of cheese.
Please skip back from the mar - ket, oh, To buy a pound of cheese.

"Choose a place in the room for the market. Take turns skipping to the market and back." "Sing about other food that you can buy at the market."

Follow the Leader

L.W.

1. Clap your hands, stamp your feet, Play on a big bass drum.
2. Touch your head, touch your chin, Play on a big bass drum.

Clap your hands, stamp your feet, Rum tum tum tum tum.
Touch your head, touch your chin, Rum tum tum tum tum.

3. Touch your ears, touch your nose, Play on a big bass drum.
   Touch your ears, touch your nose, Rum tum tum tum tum.

4. Touch your knees, touch your toes, Play on a big bass drum.
   Touch your knees, touch your toes, Rum tum tum tum tum.

Little Shadow

L.W.

Fun-ny lit-tle shad-ow, (Fun-ny lit-tle shad-ow,) Al-ways walks when I walk,
Fun-ny lit-tle shad-ow, (Fun-ny lit-tle shad-ow,) Al-ways runs when I run,

(Echo)

(Echo)

(Al-ways walks when I walk,) Fun-ny lit-tle shad-ow, (Fun-ny lit-tle shad-ow,)
(Al-ways runs when I run,) Fun-ny lit-tle shad-ow, (Fun-ny lit-tle shad-ow,)

Walk,— walk,— walk,— walk,— walk.
Run, run, run, run, run, run, run, run, run.

(Echo)

(Walk,— walk,— walk,— walk,— walk.)
(Run, run, run, run, run, run run, run, run.)

3. Claps 4. Hops 5. Jumps 6. Swings 7. Nods

"Choose someone to be your shadow."

Tip-Toe Song

Flemish Folk Tune

The Band

R.M.

"How does the music sound when the band is coming down the street and is still far away?"
"How does the music sound when it is very near?"
"How does the music sound when the band has gone past?" "When is it soft?" "When is it loud?"

Boom Boom

L.W.

Boom, boom, boom, boom, boom. We can play on the drum, drum, drum.
March-ing, march-ing,— here we come.

Bells

R.M.

One lit-tle bell said "do, do," One lit-tle bell said "mi, mi,"

One lit-tle bell said "sol, sol," Sol mi do. Ding! Ding! Ding!

Sing the do mi sol or play them on the resonator bells.
"How do they sound when played together?"
"What are the three notes played together called?" (a chord)

Tinkling Bells

R.M.

Oh, hear the sound of tink - ling bells, Ding, ding, ding.

The ring - ing sound of lit - tle bells, Ding, ding, ding,

Take the G and C resonator bells from the box so that a child may play the last two measures of each line.

The Candle

L.W.

A lit - tle can-dle cries, The lit - tle tear - drops fall.

A lit - tle can - dle cries Till there's noth-ing left at all.

Play a descending scale on the bells as an introduction to the song.
"Pretend that you are the candle and melt to the floor."

67

Balloons for Sale

Shari Davis

"Where does the harmonica play on the recording of the song?"

Blow Up a Balloon

L.W.

Funny Clown

L.W.

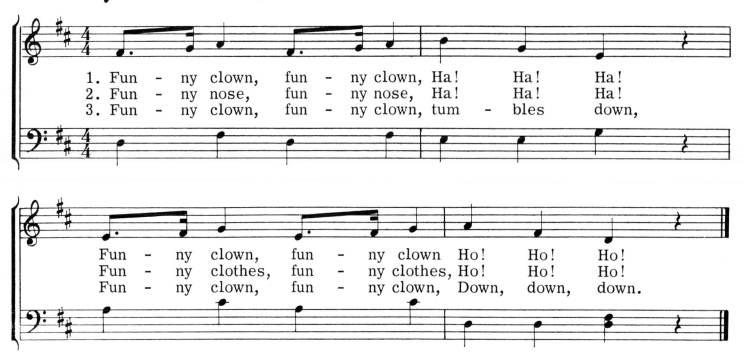

1. Fun - ny clown, fun - ny clown, Ha! Ha! Ha!
2. Fun - ny nose, fun - ny nose, Ha! Ha! Ha!
3. Fun - ny clown, fun - ny clown, tum - bles down,

Fun - ny clown, fun - ny clown Ho! Ho! Ho!
Fun - ny clothes, fun - ny clothes, Ho! Ho! Ho!
Fun - ny clown, fun - ny clown, Down, down, down.

Merry Go Round

L.W.

Steadily

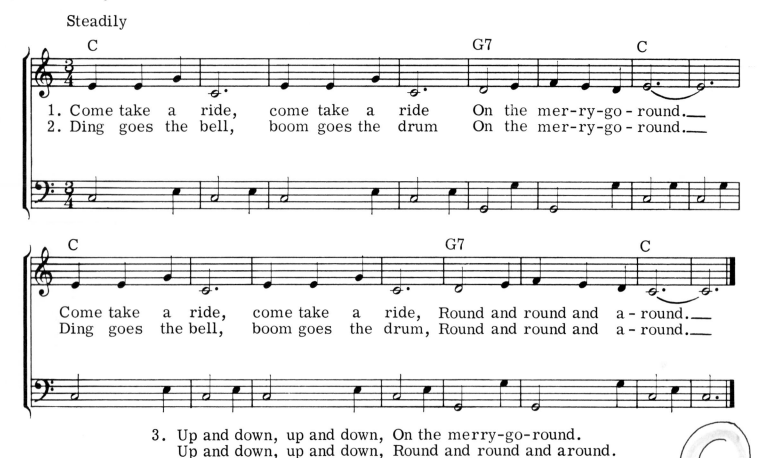

1. Come take a ride, come take a ride On the mer-ry-go-round.___
2. Ding goes the bell, boom goes the drum On the mer-ry-go-round.___

Come take a ride, come take a ride, Round and round and a-round.___
Ding goes the bell, boom goes the drum, Round and round and a-round.___

3. Up and down, up and down, On the merry-go-round.
Up and down, up and down, Round and round and around.

"Move like the animals on the merry-go-round."
Add a drum and finger cymbals to the second and third verse of the song.

Someday Very Soon

R.M.

1. When I am old-er I'll fly to the moon, fly to the moon, fly to the moon, fly to the moon, When I am old-er I'll fly to the moon, Some-day ver-y soon._____
2. When I am old-er I'll play my gui-tar, play my gui-tar, play my gui-tar, When I am old-er I'll play my gui-tar, Some-day ver-y soon._____
3. When I am old-er I'll sail in my boat, sail in my boat, sail in my boat, When I am old-er I'll sail in my boat, Some-day ver-y soon._____

"What would you like to do when you are older?" "Could we sing about it?"

When is the Day?

R.M.

Spirited

1. When is the day to be hap-py? When is the day to be
2. When is the day to be sing-ing? When is the day to be

hap-py? When is the day to be hap - py?
sing-ing? When is the day to be sing - ing?

Mon-day, Tues-day, Wednes-day, Thurs-day, Fri-day, Sat-ur - day, Sun - day!

Some children may be able to play the scale with the last phrase if the resonator bells are removed from the case.

Greetings

R.M.

1. All peo - ple give greet - ings to friends on the street,
2. "Good morn - ing, good morn - ing," so some peo - ple say,

All peo - ple give greet - ings when - ev - er they meet.
"Good morn - ing, good morn - ing, a good day to - day.

3. "Buon giorno, buon giorno," so some people say,
"Buon giorno, buon giorno, a good day today."

Playmates

R.M.

Do you have a play - mate? Oh, yes!
What___ does it say?_____ Quack, quack!

Do you have a play - mate? Oh, yes!
What___ have does it say?_____ Quack, quack!

Do you have a play - mate? Oh, yes!
What___ have does it say?_____ Quack, quack!

Tell a - bout it now.
Quack, quack, quack, quack, quack!

Telephones

L.W.

Hel - lo, hel - lo, I can hard - ly hear you. Hel-lo, hel - lo,

You are far a - way. Hel-lo, hel - lo, We will have a par - ty. Hel-

Answer

lo, hel - lo, Can you come to play? Hel - lo, hello, I can hard - ly

hear you. Hel-lo, hel-lo, You are far a - way. Hel-lo, hel - lo,

I will be right o - ver. Hel-lo, hel - lo, I can come to play.

Come and Play with Me

L.W.

1. Come and see my play - house, Come and play with me.
2. Come and see my play - house, Come and play with me.

We will make some cook - ies, Come and play with me.
We will set the ta - ble, Come and play with me.

3. We will wash the dishes, etc.

"What other things in the play house can we sing about?"

A Tea Party

Traditional

1. Come and have a cup of tea, Come and have a cup of tea,

Come and have a cup of tea and vis - it me.

2. Stir the sugar in your tea, etc.
3. Have a cookie with your tea, etc.
4. Polly (Susan) put the kettle on, etc.

Substitute names of other children in verse four.

Playing in the Sand

Traditional Tune
L.W.

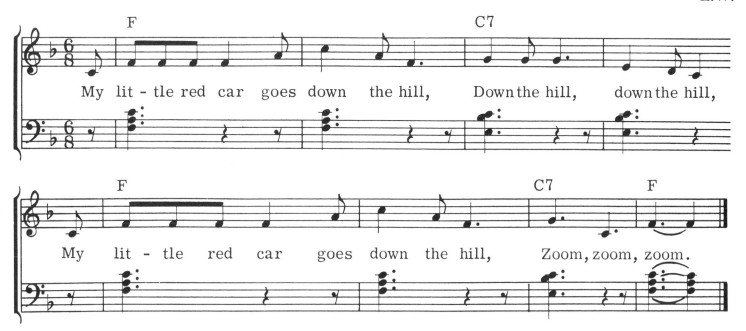

My lit - tle red car goes down the hill, Down the hill, down the hill,

My lit - tle red car goes down the hill, Zoom, zoom, zoom.

Sing about other things the little red car can do.

Don't Cry Little Dolly

L.W.

Tenderly

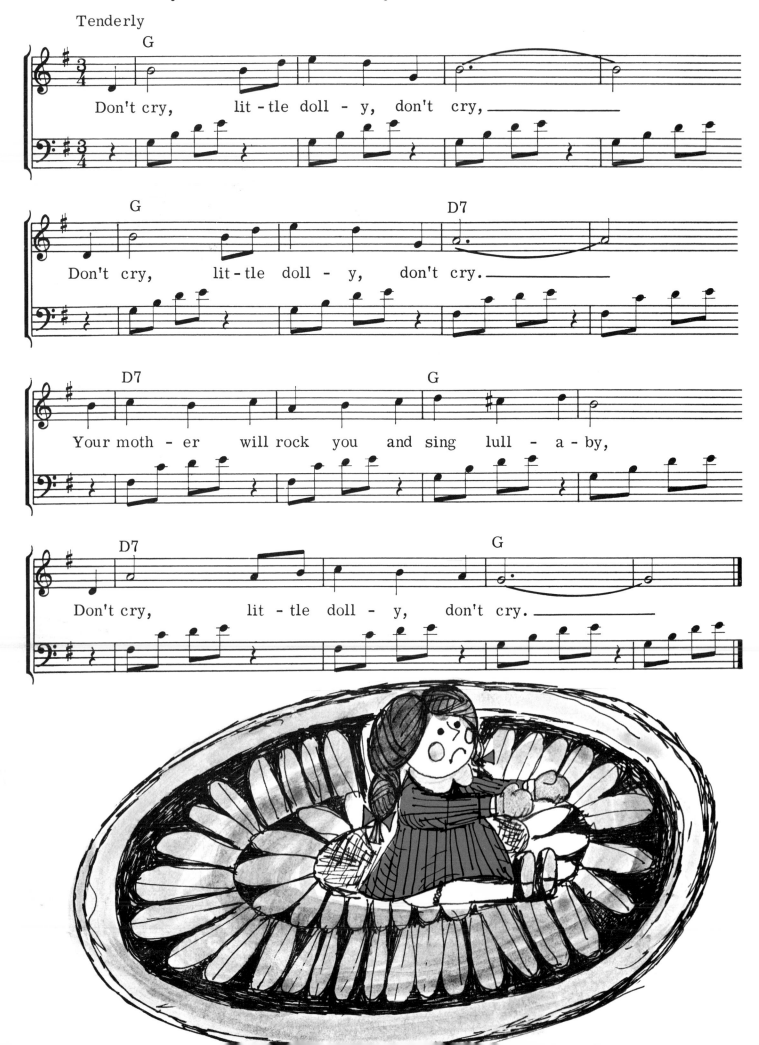

Don't cry, lit-tle doll-y, don't cry,

Don't cry, lit-tle doll-y, don't cry.

Your moth-er will rock you and sing lull-a-by,

Don't cry, lit-tle doll-y, don't cry.

Ride Cowboy Ride

R.M.

G

1. Ride, cow-boy, ride,   Ride, cow-boy,
2. Ride, cow-boy, ride,   Ride, cow-boy,
3. Ride, cow-boy, ride,   Ride, cow-boy,

A7

D7

ride,   Herd your cat - tle, herd your cat - tle,
ride,   Rope the do - gies, rope the do - gies,
ride,   Cinch your sad - dle, cinch your sad - dle,

G

Ride, cow-boy, ride!
Ride, cow-boy, ride!
Ride, cow-boy, ride!

Add other ideas of what a cowboy does such as "twirl your lariat." Play coconut shells, woodblock or walnut halves for the sound of horses' hoofs. Some children will enjoy trotting to the song. The rhythm may be changed to an uneven rhythm so that they can gallop, too.

Giddiap

L.W.

Strongly accented

1. Gid-di- ap, gid-di -ap, gid-di -ap, hor-sey, Gid-di -ap, gid -di -ap, go, go, go!
2. Gid-di- ap, gid-di -ap, gid-di -ap, hor-sey, O- ver the fence now go, go, go!

Gid-di-ap, gid-di-ap, gid -di -ap, hor-sey, Gid-di -ap, gid-di -ap, whoa, whoa.
Gid-di-ap, gid-di-ap, gid -di -ap, hor-sey, Go___ back home now, whoa, whoa.

3. Gid-di-ap, gid-di-ap, gid-di-ap, horsey, Round in a circle, go, go, go.
   Gid-di-ap, gid-di-ap, gid-di-ap, horsey, Round in a circle, go, go.

"Show how high a horse lifts his feet when he gallops."

Trot Old Joe

Texas Folk Song, sung by Anne Beyette

Leisurely

Trot, Old Joe, trot, Old Joe, You ride bet-ter'n an-y
Walk, Old Joe, walk, Old Joe, You ride bet-ter'n an-y

horse I know. Trot, Old Joe, trot, Old Joe,
horse I know. Walk, Old Joe, walk, Old Joe,

You're the best horse in the coun-try, O. Whoa, Joe!
You're the best horse in the coun-try, O. Whoa, Joe!

Pony Song

Alice G. Thorn,
Satis Coleman

See the po-ny gal-lop-ing, gal-lop-ing down the coun-try road.

Slow to end   *rit.*

See the po-ny com-ing home, all tired out, all tired out.

Ponies

R.M.

Po - nies graz - ing in the mead - ow,_____
Po - nies rest - ing in the shad - ows,_____

Po - nies graz - ing in the mead - ow,_____
Po - nies rest - ing in the shad - ows,_____

Po - nies graz - ing in the mead-ow,_____ And they gal-loped a -
Po - nies rest - ing in the shad-ows,_____

way, and they gal - loped a - way, and they gal - loped a - way!_____

1. Ponies drinking cool, clear water, etc.
2. Their black coats were smooth and shiny, etc.

Mr. Turtle

R.M.

Plodding

Mis - ter Tur - tle moves a - round, See him go.
Mis - ter Tur - tle takes his house, See him go.
Mis - ter Tur - tle goes to sleep, Ho, ho, hum.

Mis - ter Tur - tle moves a - round, Slow, slow, slow.
Mis - ter Tur - tle takes his house, Slow, slow, slow.
Mis - ter Tur - tle goes to sleep, Ho, ho, hum.

In Our Aquarium

Dutch Folk Tune

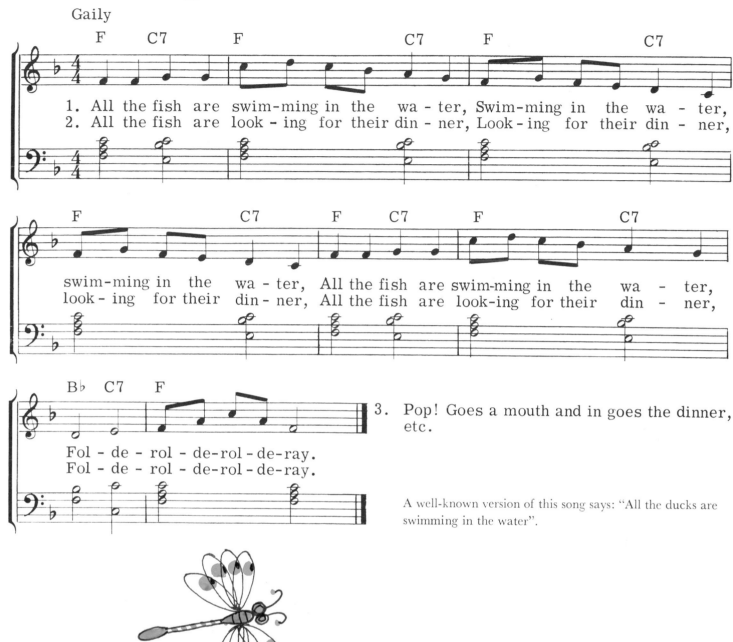

Gaily

1. All the fish are swim-ming in the wa-ter, Swim-ming in the wa-ter,
2. All the fish are look-ing for their din-ner, Look-ing for their din-ner,

swim-ming in the wa-ter, All the fish are swim-ming in the wa - ter,
look-ing for their din-ner, All the fish are look-ing for their din-ner,

Fol - de - rol - de-rol-de-ray.
Fol - de - rol - de-rol-de-ray.

3. Pop! Goes a mouth and in goes the dinner, etc.

A well-known version of this song says: "All the ducks are swimming in the water".

Kitty and Puppy

R.M.

1. One lit – tle kit – ty drinks her milk,
2. One lit – tle pup – py chews his bone,

One lit – tle kit – ty cleans her fur,
One lit – tle pup – py digs a hole,

One lit – tle kit – ty yawns and stretch – es,
One lit – tle pup – py yawns and stretch – es,

slower

One lit – tle kit – ty goes to sleep.
One lit – tle pup – py goes to sleep.

Old King Cole

Traditional

1. Old King Cole was a mer - ry old soul and a
2. Fee, fee, fee, fee,___ fee,___ old fee, fee,___

mer - ry old soul was he. He called for his pipe and he
fee,___ fee, fee, fee, fee. Fee, fee,___ fee, fee,___

called for his bowl and he called for his fid - dlers three.
fee, fee,___ fee,___ fee, fee fee, fee, fee.

Jack Be Nimble

Traditional

Jack be nim - ble, Jack be quick, Jack jump o - ver the can - dle-stick.

Diddle Diddle Dumpling

Traditional
R.M.

Did-dle, did-dle, dump - ling, my son John, Went to bed with his stock-ings on.

One shoe off and one shoe on, Did-dle, did - dle, dump-ling, my son John.

One child may play the C scale on the bells as an introduction.

Pease Porridge Hot

Traditional

Pease por-ridge hot,   Pease por-ridge cold,
Some like it hot,   Some like it cold,

Pease por-ridge in the pot   Nine days old.
Some like it in the pot   Nine days old.

See-Saw Sacradown

Traditional

Rhythmically

See - saw, Sa - cra-down, Which is the way to Lon - don Town?

One foot up and one foot down. This is the way to Lon - don Town.

Wee Willie Winkie

Nursery Song
R.M.

Wee Wil-lie Win - kie, (Wee Wil-lie Win - kie,) Runs through the town,

(Runs through the town,) Up - stairs and down-stairs, (Up - stairs and down-stairs,)

In his night - gown, (In his night - gown,) Rap-ping at the win - dow,

(Knock in rhythm) Cry - ing through the lock, (Cry - ing through the lock,)

"Are the chil-dren in their beds?"("Are the chil-dren in their beds?")

for it's eight o' - clock.— *Play bells eight times*

Goodbye My Lover Goodbye

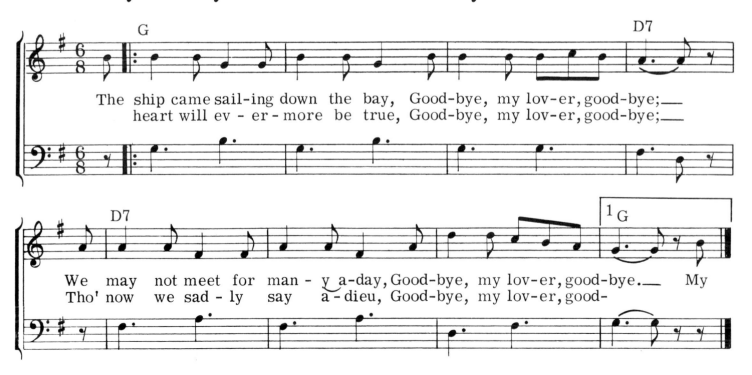

The ship came sail-ing down the bay, Good-bye, my lov-er, good-bye;___
heart will ev - er - more be true, Good-bye, my lov-er, good-bye;___

We may not meet for man - y a-day, Good-bye, my lov-er, good-bye.___ My
Tho' now we sad - ly say a - dieu, Good-bye, my lov-er, good-

2. Then cheer up till we meet again, Goodbye, my lover, goodbye;
I'll try to bear my weary pain, Goodbye, my lover, goodbye.
Though far I roam across the sea, Goodbye, my lover, goodbye,
My ev'ry thought of you shall be, Goodbye, my lover, goodbye!

In Our Rowboat

R.M.

Deliberately

Row to-geth-er, row to-geth-er, row, row, row,
Rest a-while and rest a-while and float, float, float,
Pull to-geth-er, pull to-geth-er, pull the oar,

Row to-geth-er, row to-geth-er, yo, ho, ho!
Rock and rock and rock and rock in our row-boat.
Pull to-geth-er, pull to-geth-er, home once more!

Bobby Shafto

Traditional

Bob-by Shaf-to's gone to sea, Sil-ver buck-les on his knee.

He'll come back and mar-ry me,— Dear Bob-by Shaf-to.

Working on the Railroad

American Folk Song

I've been work-ing on the rail - road, All the live - long day;

I've been work-ing on the rail - road, To pass the time a - way.

Don't you hear the whis-tle blow - in', Rise up so ear-ly in the morn;

Don't you hear the cap-tain shout - in' "Di - nah, blow your horn."

Big Black Train

L.W.

Big black train, Big black train, Take me up the moun - tain.
Big black train, Big black train, Take me to the coun - try.

Big black train, Big black train, Take me down a - gain.
Big black train, Big black train, Take me home a - gain.

Chug Chug Chug

L.W.

Chug, chug, chug, chug, chug, chug, chug, chug, Choo, choo, choo.
Ding, ding, ding, ding, ding, ding, ding, ding, Ding, ding, ding.

Chug, chug, chug, chug, chug, chug, chug, chug,
Ding, ding, ding, ding, ding, ding, ding, ding,

Choo, choo, choo, choo, choo.
Ding, ding, ding, ding, dong.

Little Red Caboose

Traditional

Lit - tle red ca - boose, Lit - tle red ca - boose,

Lit - tle red ca - boose be - hind the train,___ the train,___

Smoke stack on his back, go - ing down the track,

Lit - tle red ca - boose be - hind the train. (Too - too - too)

The Fire Truck

Traditional Tune
L.W.

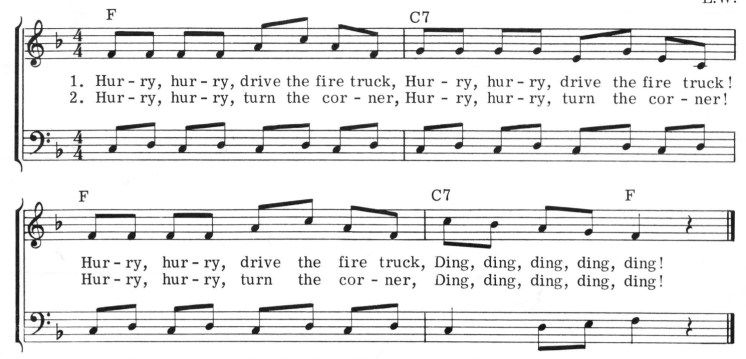

1. Hur - ry, hur - ry, drive the fire truck, Hur - ry, hur - ry, drive the fire truck!
2. Hur - ry, hur - ry, turn the cor - ner, Hur - ry, hur - ry, turn the cor - ner!

Hur - ry, hur - ry, drive the fire truck, Ding, ding, ding, ding, ding!
Hur - ry, hur - ry, turn the cor - ner, Ding, ding, ding, ding, ding!

3. Hurry, hurry, find the fire, Hurry, hurry, find the fire!
Hurry, hurry, find the fire, Ding, ding, ding, ding, ding!

4. Hurry, hurry, climb the ladder, hurry, hurry, climb the ladder!
Hurry, hurry, climb the ladder, Ding, ding, ding, ding, ding!

5. Hurry, hurry, squirt the water, Hurry, hurry, squirt the water!
Hurry, hurry, squirt the water, Ding, ding, ding, ding, ding!

"Choose an instrument to play with the bell sound."
Play the last five pitches of the song on the five resonator bells which have been removed from the set and placed in a box that can be passed around from child to child.

98

Little Red Engine

L.W.

Lit-tle red en-gine hur-ried through town,

Some-one's house was burn-ing down!

Lit-tle red en-gine said with a shout,

"We will put the fire out!"

In My Plane

R.M.

Smoothly

Clouds go drift - ing by,   La - zy in the sky,

Soar - ing up so high,   My air - plane and I.

I Can Fly

L.W.

Brightly

Big Yellow Bus

R.M.

1. A big yel-low bus goes to my school, to my school, to my school,
2. The big yel-low bus will come for me, come for me, come for me,

A big yel-low bus goes to my school ev' - ry day.
The big yel-low bus will come for me ev' - ry day.

3. The driver of the bus is my good friend, etc.
4. The children on the bus are happy, too, etc.

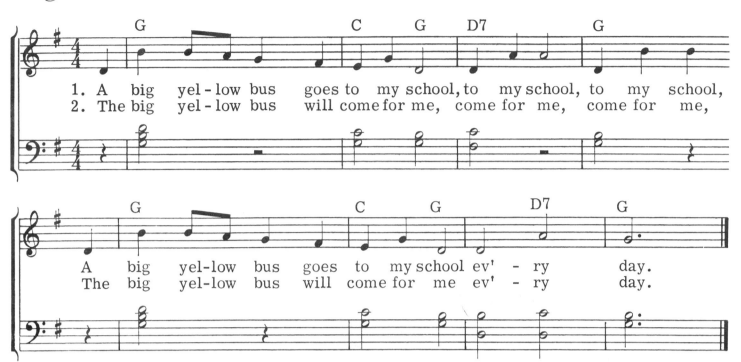

Look at Us

Trudi Behar

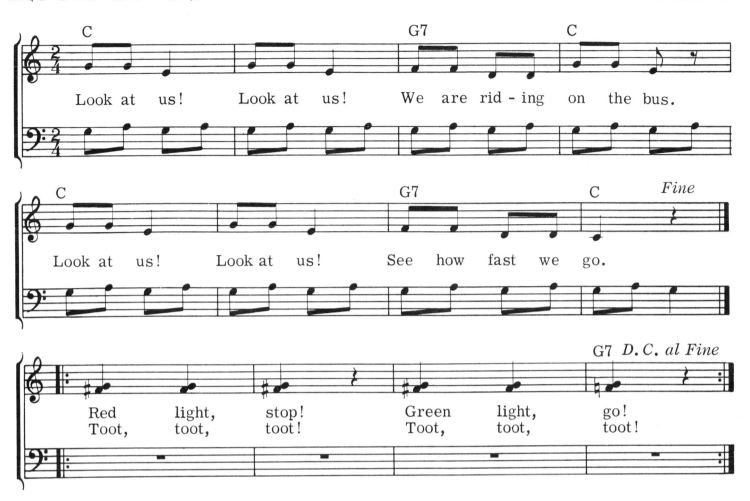

Look at us! Look at us! We are rid - ing on the bus.

Look at us! Look at us! See how fast we go.

Red light, stop! Green light, go!
Toot, toot, toot! Toot, toot, toot!

My Guitar

R.M.

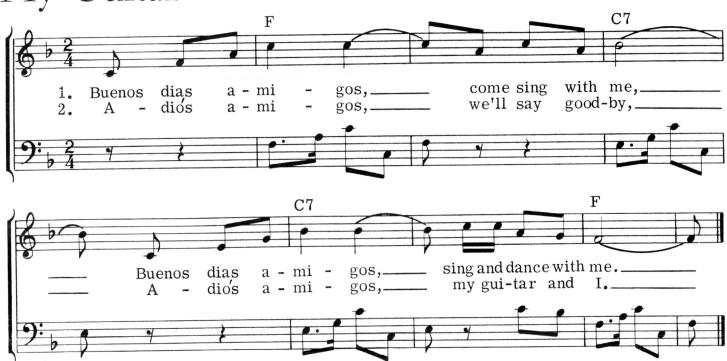

1. Buenos dias a - mi - gos,_____ come sing with me,_____
2. A - diós a - mi - gos,_____ we'll say good-by,_____

_____ Buenos dias a - mi - gos,_____ sing and dance with me._____
_____ A - diós a - mi - gos,_____ my gui-tar and I._____

As a third stanza, boys hum and play guitars while the girls dance.

104

When You Sing

Rhythmically

Tehuantepec

1. When you sing, tra la, ____ when you sing, tra la, ____
2. When you dance, tra la, ____ when you dance, tra la, ____

When you sing you are nev - er sad, ____
When you dance you are nev - er sad, ____

When you sing, tra la, ____ when you sing, tra la, ____
When you dance, tra la, ____ when you dance, tra la, ____

When you sing you will al - ways be glad. ____
When you dance you will al - ways be glad. ____

Play finger cymbals or triangle with the first stanza; tambourine and sticks with the second stanza.

Chiapanecas

Mexican Folk Tune

1. Ay, Chia - pa - ne - cas, ay, ay! (clap, clap)

Ay, Chia - pa - ne - cas, ay, ay! (clap, clap)

Ay, Chia - pa - ne - cas, ay, ay! (clap, clap)

Ay, Chia - pa - ne - cas, ay, ay! (clap, clap)

2: *"Sing, Chiapanecas, ay, ay - ", etc.*
3: *"Dance, Chiapanecas, ay, ay - ", etc.*
The most inexperienced small singers will join in with the clapping. They may select a percussion instrument to play on the clapping notes.

Patriotic Medley

Traditional

March-like

G   D7   G   D7

Yan - kee Doo - dle went to town a - rid - ing on a po - ny, He

G   C   D7   G

stuck a feath - er in his cap and called it mac - a - ro - ni.

C   G

Yan - kee Doo - dle keep it up, Yan - kee Doo - dle dan - dy,

C   G   D7   G

Mind the mu - sic and the step and with the girls be han - dy!

Thomas Beckett

Spirited

Three cheers for the Red, White and Blue! Three__ cheers for the Red, White and Blue! The__ flag of our coun - try for - ev - er, Three cheers for the Red, White and Blue!